TO = CHRIS

HENNIE VAESSEN

22 = 9 = 2013

THE BATTLE OF ARNHEM
SEPTEMBER 1944

Part 3:
Eagle and Pegasus

Imprint:

The Battle of Arnhem. September 1944
A Graphic Novel

Part 3: Eagle and Pegasus

Text and illustrations:	Hennie Vaessen
Colouring:	Studio Vaessen: Jan, Tine and Hennie
Publisher:	Pelikaanpers, Oosterbeek: www.pelikaanpers.nl
German translation:	Drs. Ingrid Maan, www.betweendutchdeutsch.nl
English translation:	Graeme Cunningham, www.nativespeakerengels.nl
Polish translation:	Dr. Iwona Guść, researcher at NIOD

ISBN: 978-94-9000-13-4
NUR: 689

Dutch text available on: www.graphicnovel1944.com

This book is printed on FSC paper

STANISŁAW SOSABOWSKI

*MONTY: FIELD MARSHAL MONTGOMERY

THE WESTERN FRONT? MAY I REMIND YOU, GENERAL...

...WITH ALL DUE RESPECT SIR, THESE MEN TRAIN AND PREPARE WITH THE SOLE AIM OF LIBERATING OUR POOR HOMELAND POLAND!

I KNOW! AND I HAVE NO DOUBTS ABOUT YOUR PATRIOTISM, GENERAL, HOWEVER... WE'VE LITTLE CHOICE.

WE NEED YOUR MEN.

LOOK AT YOUR MEN! THEY ARE FULL OF BINGE,* THEY'RE READY TO KILL ANYONE WHO CROSSES THEIR PATH!

SIR... I MUST REMIND YOU THAT THE AUTHORITY TO DECIDE OVER THEM LIES WITH THE POLISH GOVERNMENT IN EXILE...

...AND WITH THE POLISH GOVERNMENT ONLY, SIR!

HMM...

I DISAGREE, BUT LET'S NOT GET INTO A QUARREL, GENERAL SOSABOWSKI.

NO SIR...

ONLY ENEMIES...

*BINGE: MONTGOMERY"S TERM FOR SOLDIERS FULL OF FIGHTING SPIRIT.

LUITENANT DYRDRA?

MY WIFE, GENERAL!

?!

WHO IS THAT WOMAN THAT KEEPS WALKING UP AND DOWN AT THIS TIME OF NIGHT?

YOUR WIFE? OH! HOW SELFISH OF ME. MY WORKING LATE IS KEEPING YOU FROM YOUR DOMESTIC DUTIES.

BUT I HAVE NO TIME TO LOSE, DYRDRA. HOW ELSE CAN I PREPARE A BATTLE IN LESS THAN 5 DAYS?

AND THAT WHILE IT TOOK THEM 5 MONTHS TO PLAN SOMETHING SIMILAR ON D-DAY...

BUT STILL, I HAVE TO DO IT.

GENERAL?

YES, WHAT IS IT, DYRDRA?

MY WIFE ASKED ME LAST NIGHT WHICH PLANE I WOULD BE GOING IN. AND WHEN I TOLD HER THAT OF COURSE I WOULD BE GOING IN YOURS, SHE SAID: THANK GOD!

THEN AT LEAST NOTHING CAN HAPPEN TO YOU. THE OLD SOSAB IS ALWAYS LUCKY.

ACH! DYRDRA.

LET'S HOPE THAT YOUR WIFE'S RIGHT,...

OFF YOU GO! GET AWAY HOME NOW.

UNTIL TOMORROW, GENERAL.

THE DRIEL FERRY

EVERY DAY SOLDIERS ARE DYING IN THE NETHERLANDS AND WE CAN DO NOTHING... STUCK HERE IN THIS DAMNED FOG!!

FLIGHT POSTPONED FOR 24 HOURS! DUE TO BAD WEATHER!

?! !!

!! ?!

THE MEN ARE STARTING TO LOSE THEIR GRIP... I'M AFRAID THEY'LL DO SOMETHING STUPID IF WE DON'T LEAVE TOMORROW...

BACK TO THE BARRACKS...

NIECH TO SZLAG!!

THIS IS THE THIRD TIME ALREADY.

...MAYBE WE'LL HAVE BETTER LUCK TOMORROW...

DAMNED FOG!

○ 21ST SEPTEMBER...

SIR! NEWS FROM HOLLAND!

?!

IT SEEMS LIKE THE MEN AT THE BRIDGE HAVE NOT BEEN ABLE TO HOLD OUT. GENERAL URQUHART IS STUCK IN OOSTERBEEK AND IN DESPERATE NEED OF REINFORCEMENTS!

YOUR TROOPS ARE STILL TO BE DROPPED SOUTH OF THE RHINE! BUT NOW YOU'LL CROSS AT THE DRIEL FERRY!

RIGHT!

TSJAK!!

THERE'S **NO** OTHER WAY...

...WHATEVER HAPPENS, THE GERMANS MUSTN'T GET THEIR HANDS ON THE FERRY.

BUT PETER,...

...YOU'RE FORGETTING SOMETHING...

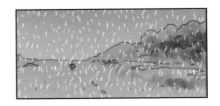

...HOW ARE THE TOMMIES GOING TO CROSS THE RIVER NOW?

JANEK! THOSE PEOPLE ARE WAVING AT US.

TAK! THEY'RE HAPPY WE'RE HERE.

WHAT ARE THOSE SMALL WHITE CLOUDS?

THAT'S FLAK! WE'RE UNDER FIRE.

BOŻE DROGI...

DON'T WORRY! JUST LOOK AT THE OLD SOSABOWSKI!

HE'S A PICTURE OF PEACE, AS IF HE'S LYING IN BED AT HOME!

BOŻE DROGI, I CAN'T LET THEM SEE HOW SCARED I AM.

NO, SZYMON...

...WITH OLD SOSA AROUND NOTHING CAN HAPPEN TO US.

ŚWIETA MARYJO MATKO BOŻA

POMOCY!

FLOP

OOF!

TAKTAK

TAK

TAKTAK

DO DIABŁA! THAT SPANDAU* MUST BE DEALT WITH IMMEDIATELY!

TAKTAKTAK

?
?
?

TAKTAK...

CHOLERNE SZWABY!

YOUR WAR IS OVER!

SPANDAU OUT OF ACTION, GENERAL.

GOOD, WELL DONE.

SEND A RECONNAISSANCE PATROL TO THE DRIEL FERRY AND CALL GENERAL URQUHART AT ONCE.

YES, GENERAL!

FOX, BAKER, OBOE DO YOU READ ME, DO YOU READ ME? OVER!

*SPANDAU: GERMAN MG42 7.9MM MACHINE GUN

POLES IN DRIEL

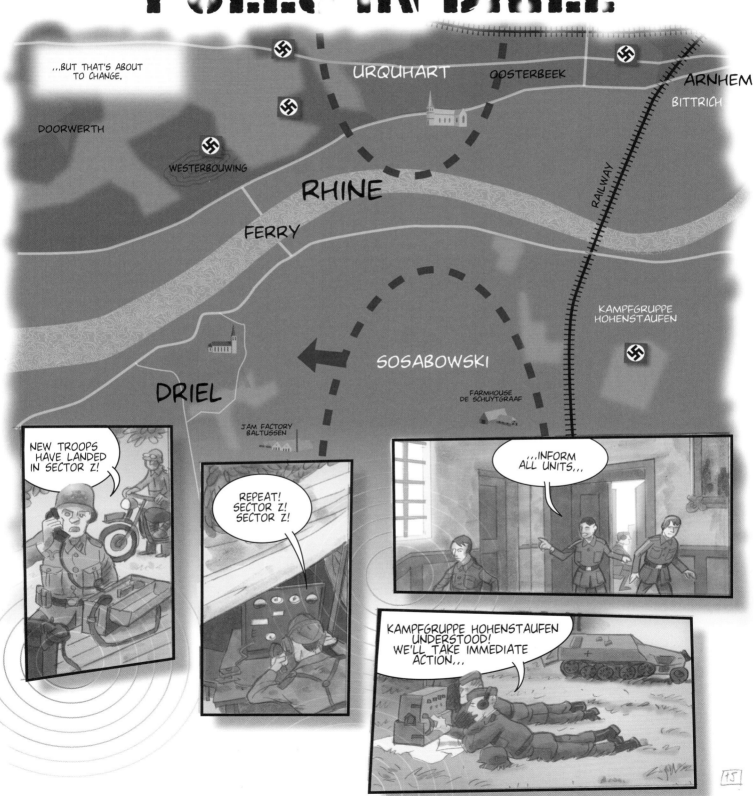

MAKE IT CLEAR TO THESE PEOPLE THAT THEY ARE NOW IN THE MIDDLE OF A BLOODY WAR!!

GENERAL! GENERAL!

LATER SOSABOWSKI HEADQUARTERS

GENERAL! THE FERRY IS GONE!

?

GENERAL! GERMAN TROOPS APPROACHING FROM THE WEST!

DAMN! THAT'S WHAT I WAS AFRAID OF. WE'RE GOING TO BE STUCK HERE!

LISTEN, THIS IS WHAT WE'LL DO...

GENERAL!

BWAM

WHO'S MAKING ALL THAT RACKET?!

AH... UM...? ZWOLAŃSKI?? IS THAT YOU?

GENERAL... NEWS FROM THE OTHER SIDE, FROM GENERAŁ URQUHART!

WE SAW YOU COMING AND TRIED TO CONTACT YOU BUT GOT NO CONNECTION...

I IMMEDIATELY OFFERED TO SWIM ACROSS THE RHINE...

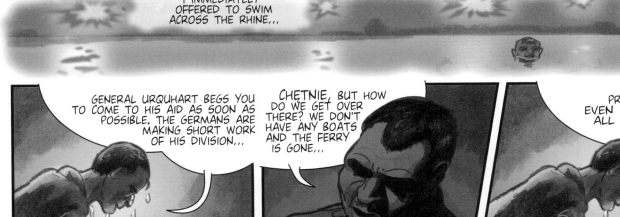

GENERAL URQUHART BEGS YOU TO COME TO HIS AID AS SOON AS POSSIBLE. THE GERMANS ARE MAKING SHORT WORK OF HIS DIVISION...

CHĘTNIE, BUT HOW DO WE GET OVER THERE? WE DON'T HAVE ANY BOATS AND THE FERRY IS GONE...

PROSZĘ, GENERAL, EVEN 10 MEN CAN MAKE ALL THE DIFFERENCE...

YOU'RE RIGHT... TELL THE GENERAL WE'LL BE THERE...

TONIGHT! WE'LL FIND A WAY!

DZIĘKUJĘ, THANK YOU. I'LL SWIM BACK WITH YOUR ANSWER!

17

NEAR NIJMEGEN, TWO DAYS LATER, 23RD SEPTEMBER'

GEORGE? WHATEVER IN THE WORLD ARE YOU DOING DOWN THERE?

HEADQUARTERS GENERAL BROWNING

TAKING COVER, SORRY, SIR... I WAS UNDER THE IMPRESSION THAT WE WERE UNDER FIRE...

NONSENSE!

WE HAD A LOT WORSE IN SICILY! NOW, GIVE ME YOUR REPORT!

WELL, SIR...

THE HUNS ARE TRYING TO DRIVE US OUT OF THESE HILLS USING EVERYTHING THEY'VE GOT, I DON'T KNOW WHERE THEY'RE GETTING THEIR TROOPS FROM...

HMM...

ANNOYING TO BE FIGHTING OLD MEN AND CHILDREN. AH WELL... I DID COME HERE TO SEE SOME ACTION,

ANY NEWS FROM URQUHART?

SAME STORY, SIR, HIS DIVISION IS HANGING ON BY ITS FINGERNAILS. BARELY HOLDING OUT...

HOW ABOUT THE POLES?

WHY DOESN'T SOSABOWSKI DO SOMETHING?

THEY'VE TRIED TO CROSS THE RHINE THREE TIMES SO FAR, SWIMMING AND USING IMPROVISED RAFTS...

...A FEW HUNDRED MEN HAVE SUCCEEDED TO GET ACROSS AT THE COST OF MANY LIVES.

THEY SEEM TO BE STUCK AT DRIEL.

WELL, THAT'S NOT GOOD ENOUGH, THEY SHALL HAVE TO TRY HARDER!

EVERYBODY HAS TO TAKE THAT EXTRA STEP.

I'LL SEE TO IT MYSELF, JUST AS SOON AS I'VE CLEARED THIS MESS UP.

SOSABOWSKI
MAKES AN INSPECTION TOUR
OF HIS TROOPS...

...ON AN OLD LADIES' BIKE...

...TO THE AMUSEMENT
OF HIS MEN.

?!

GENERAL?!

THE BRITISH COMMAND WOULD LIKE TO HAVE A WORD WITH YOU.

?

THE NEXT MORNING SOSABOWSKI BREAKS THROUGH THE GERMAN POSITIONS AT TOP SPEED (IN ORDER TO AVOID ENEMY FIRE) ON HIS WAY TO MEET THE HIGH COMMAND.

VROAWW

THE VALBURG CONFERENCE

WE'RE SITTING DUCKS! FROM UP ON THE WESTERBOUWING THE GERMANS HAVE THE WHOLE AREA COVERED.

THIS MUST BE IT GENERAL.

VROAAA

I MUST CONVICE THE BRITISH THAT WE HAVE TO CROSS THE RHINE FROM A MORE WESTERLY POSITION, PREFERABLY WITH A WHOLE DIVISION!

?!

?

AH, SOSABOWSKI ...

...DO SIT DOWN.

YOUR TRANSLATOR CAN STAND BEHIND YOU!

IT LOOKS MORE LIKE A COURT MARTIAL!

GENTLEMEN!

GENERAL URQUHART'S DIVISION IS IN GRAVE DANGER. SO FAR THE POLISH LANDINGS HAVE PROVED UNSUCCESSFUL!

?

THEREFORE I NOW GIVE THE ORDER FOR TWO MORE RHINE CROSSINGS! THE 4TH BATTALION DORSETS WILL MAKE THE FIRST CROSSING...

...FOLLOWED BY THE FIRST POLISH BATTALION.

NO! THEY WANT TO SPLIT UP MY MEN!

THE CROSSINGS WILL TAKE PLACE AT THE DRIEL FERRY, TONIGHT!

YES? GENERAL SOSABOWSKI?

GENERAŁOWIE! Z CAŁYM SZACUNKIEM... NIE POŚWIĘCAJCIE NASZYCH ŻOŁNIERZY.

MY GENERAL SAYS: WITH ALL DUE RESPECT SIRS BUT...

THANK YOU!

THE ACTIONS WILL BE PERFORMED THE WAY I JUST SAID AT THE POSITIONS I DESCRIBED!

I THANK YOU, GENTLEMEN!

!

GENERAŁOWIE!

DO NOT SACRIFICE OUR SOLDIERS!

?!?

YOU WON'T GAIN ANYTHING WITH IT! ONE BATTALION WON'T MAKE ANY DIFFERENCE! A WHOLE DIVISION MUST MAKE THE CROSSING!

THIS CONFERENCE IS OVER!

GENERAL BROWNING'S ORDERS WILL BE FULFILLED!

...REMEMBER, GENERAŁOWIE... FOR EIGHT DAYS AND NIGHTS NOW NOT ONLY POLISH SOLDIERS HAVE BEEN DYING BUT ALSO BRITAIN'S BEST SONS!

ENOUGH OF THIS!

IF YOU, GENERAL SOSABOWSKI, WILL NOT FULFILL THEM, THEN WE WILL FIND SOMEONE ELSE TO TAKE THE COMMAND OF THE POLISH AIRBORNE TROOPS!

I HOPE I AM MAKING MYSELF QUITE CLEAR...

...WHAT ARE WE GOING TO DO NOW GENERAL?

VROAAAAA

NOTHING LIEUTENANT...

...WE GO BACK TO OUR POSITIONS AND DO WHAT WE ARE TOLD!

24TH SEPTEMBER, 21:00 HOURS

CAREFUL...

THAT NIGHT TWO CANADIAN TRUCKS WITH BOATS CAUTIOUSLY MAKE THEIR WAY TOWARDS THE RHINE.

TURN RIGHT...

ARE YOU SURE?

YES...

...BECAUSE I'D HATE TO RUN INTO ANY GERMANS. THE TROOPS AT THE RHINE ARE DESPERATE FOR THESE BOATS, YOU KNOW.

STOP TALKING NONSENSE AND DRIVE!

TURN LEFT!

...MY NAVIGATIONAL SKILLS ARE FAMOUS THROUGHOUT THE ARMY!

YEAH, I BET!

THERE? WHAT DID I TELL YOU?

THANK GOD!

HELLO!!

?

DON'T JUST STAND THERE!

QUICKLY, HELP UNLOAD THESE BOATS!

HÄNDE HOCH! ENGLISH SWINE!

?!!

...NAVIGATIONAL SKILLS FAMOUS THROUGHOUT THE ARMY...

IMBECILE!

23

DRIEL,
21:50 HOURS

GENERAL! OUR BOATS HAVE ARRIVED BUT THE GERMANS HAVE GOT HOLD OF THE DORSETS' BOATS!

?!

THE DORSETS' CROSSING IS THE MOST IMPORTANT...

THEY'RE CARRYING THE MOST SUPPLIES.

DOBRA!

MEN! OUR CROSSING IS CANCELLED! WE HAVE TO TAKE OUR BOATS TO THE DORSETS!

FOR THE DORSETS IT TURNS INTO A NIGHT THEY WON'T FORGET IN A HURRY!

SO MUCH TIME HAS ALREADY BEEN LOST THAT THE GERMANS ON THE HIGHER NORTH BANK REALISE SOMETHING IS ABOUT TO HAPPEN...

...THEY GUARD THE RHINE INTENSIVELY AND SET OFF FLARES THAT CAST A BRIGHT GLOW OVER THE SURROUNDINGS, INCLUDING THE 300 DORSETS ATTEMPTING TO CROSS THE RIVER...

...MANY MEN ARE HIT IN THE HEAVY FIRE. DOZENS OF BOATS DRIFT AROUND -UNMANNED.

THAT NIGHT NOT A SINGLE OUNCE OF SUPPLIES OR MUNITIONS REACHES ROY URQUHART'S MEN...

THE BRITISH HIGH COMMAND REALISES THAT THE BRIDGEHEAD NORTH OF THE RIVER CANNOT BE MAINTAINED ...

BRITISH PERIMETER

RHINE

ON 25TH SEPTEMBER GENERAL URQUHART RECEIVES THE ORDER FOR COMPLETE WITHDRAWAL.

THE CROSSING

LIEUTENANT THERE'S A MESSAGE FOR THE GENERAL!

?

SOSABOWSKI IS SLEEPING. HE'S BEEN ON THE GO FOR THREE DAYS AND NIGHTS NOW.

IS IT URGENT?

OF COURSE! IT'S FROM HIGH COMMAND!

DOBRA! I'LL GO AND WAKE HIM!

?!!

BWAOEM

??!!

MATKO ŚWIĘTA! WHAT A HIT!

LIEUTENANT! WHERE ARE YOU?

HE'S DEAD!

THE GENERAL?! WHERE'S THE GENERAL?

GET SOME LIGHT IN HERE! WE'VE GOT CASUALTIES!

?

?!

THERE HE IS!

I KNEW IT! LADY LUCK WOULD NEVER DESERT SOSABOWSKI!

COUGH

GENERAL AN URGENT MESSAGE FROM HIGH COMMAND!

DAWAJ HAND IT OVER!

2S

26

TONIGHT AT 22:00 HOURS ALL TROOPS NORTH OF THE RHINE ARE TO WITHDRAW...

THE RHINE, NIGHT OF 25-26TH SEPTEMBER

27

THAT NIGHT, DUE TO THE COVERING FIRE FROM THE POLISH EAGLE, MORE THAN 2,000 BRITISH SERVICEMEN SUCCEED IN SAFELY REACHING THE OTHER SIDE.

DRIEL, JAM FACTORY, 26TH SEPTEMBER, 05:00 HOURS

THESE POOR BOYS ARE EXHAUSTED... HURRY! MORE BLANKETS AND RUM!

THANK YOU MADAM THIS FRUIT TASTES LIKE HEAVEN! I RAN OUT OF RATIONS THREE DAYS AGO.

I GOT WOUNDED, BUT LUCKILY MY MATES MANAGED TO DRAG ME ACROSS.

IT'S A MIRACLE WE'RE STILL ALIVE. GOD BLESS THE POLES.

MY BOAT WAS HIT. I HAD TO SWIM FOR IT. A LOT OF MEN DROWNED. IT WAS A NIGHTMARE.

I ALWAYS FELT THAT THIS WHOLE AFFAIR WAS A DISASTER RIGHT FROM THE START...

WHEN THE BOATS STOPPED, THERE WERE STILL HUNDREDS OF MEN WAITING ON THE SHORE... I ONLY MADE IT BY SWIMMING.

I SAW THIS BLOKE DROWN... THE WEIGHT OF HIS KILT DRAGGED HIM DOWN.

ARE WE ON SAFE GROUND HERE?

NO, NOT YET...

NOT UNTIL WE REACH NIJMEGEN...

HOW DO WE GET THERE?

IS IT FAR?

ONLY 15 MILES.

SORRY, BOYS, WE WALK.

LET'S GO!

WHAT
ARE THEY?

I'M NOT SURE,
THEY SEEM TO
BE BRITISH...

DO DIABŁA,
WHAT A
DISASTER...

WHO'LL GET
THE BLAME
FOR THIS??

WHO???

51

THE PERIMETER IS NOW ENTIRELY IN GERMAN HANDS, NOT ALL THE TOMMIES HAVE MANAGED TO CROSS THE RHINE. MOST OF THE WOUNDED, CHAPLAINS AND MEDICAL PERSONNEL HAVE NO CHOICE BUT TO STAY...

VICTORS AND VANQUISHED

AS THE REMAINING BRITISH TROOPS ARE TAKEN AWAY, SOME OF THE GERMANS CELEBRATE THEIR VICTORY ON THE UTRECHTSEWEG, DRIVING AROUND IN CAPTURED JEEPS AND DRINKING HEAVILY.

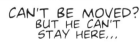
IN A CELLAR SOMEWHERE IN OOSTERBEEK...

AND DOCTOR?

ONE MOMENT...

GOT IT!

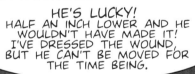
HE'S LUCKY! HALF AN INCH LOWER AND HE WOULDN'T HAVE MADE IT! I'VE DRESSED THE WOUND, BUT HE CAN'T BE MOVED FOR THE TIME BEING.

CAN'T BE MOVED? BUT HE CAN'T STAY HERE...

HE'S COMING ROUND!

WHERE AM I? AM I DEAD?

I AM SORRY, BUT I HAVE TO GO NOW ...

32

I WISH YOU LUCK.

WAIT DOCTOR! LET ME HELP YOU.

— —T — UN — —
—O — RB — S —T —
—A — — SS — G — —
— — S-R — — —

?

?

ACHTUNG! ACHTUNG! OOSTERBEEK WIRD SPERRGEBIET! ALLE MÜSSEN WEG! SOFORT!

ACHTUNG! ACHTUNG! OOSTERBEEK WIRD SPERRGEBIET! ALLE MÜSSEN WEG! SOFORT! ACHTUNG! ACH...

!?

!?

OOSTERBEEK WIRD SPERRGEBIET!

WHAT DOES THAT MEAN, JAN, SPERRGEBIET?

IT MEANS THAT THE HUNS WANT US ALL TO LEAVE...

BUT... MY GOD! WHAT NOW? WHERE CAN WE GO? AND WHAT'S GOING TO HAPPEN TO HIM??

LISTEN ...

DON'T WORRY ABOUT ME... I'LL GO BACK TO MY UNIT, AND...

AAAAA

JACK!

WE CAN'T JUST LEAVE HIM HERE LIKE THIS...

...BUT HE CAN'T WALK EITHER.

LISTEN! I'VE GOT AN IDEA! GET MY OLD COAT FROM UPSTAIRS AND MY HAT...

33

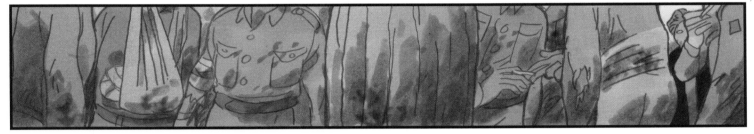

MANY BRITISH SOLDIERS WHO FAILED TO MAKE THE CROSSING ARE NOW STRANDED IN OOSTERBEEK.

DAMN IT!!

HALT!!

PAPERS!

EIN TOMMY!

I AM A DUTCHMAN! I KEINE PAPIEREN! BLOODY HELL...

KILL HIM AT ONCE! THAT'S WHAT I SAY!

LET ME TAKE CARE OF...

ONE MOMENT!

DANKE...

? ? ?

FLASH

GUT... TAKE HIM TO THE OTHERS AND THE COMMANDANT CAN DECIDE WHAT TO DO WITH HIM!!

OOF!

SOLDIERS WITHOUT UNIFORM CAN BE IMMEDIATELY EXECUTED AS SPIES BECAUSE THEY ARE NO LONGER PROTECTED BY THE GENEVA CONVENTION.

THE INTERVENTION OF A PASSING GERMAN WAR PHOTOGRAPHER JUST HAPPENS TO SAVE CAPTAIN BARRY INGRAM'S LIFE.

OOSTERBEEK, DREYENSEWEG, 26TH SEPTEMBER

DON'T LOOK, TRUUS...

LUCKY THAT WE STILL HAD THE OLD CART...

JACK DOESN'T STAND OUT AMONGST ALL THESE PEOPLE.

ANYWAY, THE HUNS HAVE GOT PLENTY OTHER THINGS TO WORRY ABOU...

HALT!

HALT! YOU THERE WITH THE CART...

?!

37

THE BATTLE OF ARNHEM
IS OVER.
TIME TO TAKE STOCK.

FACTS AND FIGURES

...APPROXIMATELY 13,000 ALLIED TROOPS FOUGHT IN THE BATTLE...

...ABOUT 1500 ALLIED WERE KILLED IN ACTION.

...AND APPROXIMATELY 14,000 GERMAN SOLDIERS,

ON THE GERMAN SIDE THE DEATH TOLL AMOUNTED TO ABOUT 1600 MEN.

THE FIGHTING ALSO COST THE LIVES OF 500 AROUND CIVILIANS,...

...AND PLUNGED ARNHEM AND MANY VELÜWEZOOM VILLAGES INTO UTTER CHAOS.

FOR GENERAL SOSABOWSKI THE BATTLE OF ARNHEM HAS A RATHER UNPLEASANT AFTERMATH...

GENERAL BROWNING?

AH, MRS WHITE. DO COME IN.

ENGLAND, AIRBORNE CORPS HEADQUARTERS, 20TH NOVEMBER 1944

WOULD YOU PLEASE TYPE A LETTER FOR ME? STRICTLY CONFIDENTIAL.

CERTAINLY, SIR.

READY, SIR.

OKAY... IT'S FOR GENERAL WEEKS, DEPUTY CHIEF OFFICER OF THE IMPERIAL GENERAL STAFF.

TICK TICK TICK TICK TICK

TICK TICK

SIR, I HAVE THE HONOUR TO BRING THE FOLLOWING FACTS TO YOUR NOTICE CONCERNING MAJOR GENERAL SOSABOWSKI DURING OPERATION "MARKET"...

Major General Sosabowski proved himself to be extremely difficult to work with. The "difficulty" was apparant not only to the commanders under whom he was planning but also to staff officers of the other Airborne formations concerned.

under whom he was planning to staff officers of the other Airborne formations concerned.

It became apparant that, capable soldier as this officer undoubtdly is, he was unable to adapt himself to the level of a parachute commander. This officer proved himself to be both argumentative and

both argumentative and loathe to play his part in the operation unless everything was done for him and his brigade. This officer worried both me and my staff who were fighting a very difficult battle to keep the corridor open about such things as two or three lorries to supplement his transport.

47

BOXING DAY, 1944

GENERAL SOSABOWSKI HANDS OVER COMMAND OF THE FIRST INDEPENDENT POLISH PARACHUTE BRIGADE TO HIS SUCCESSOR.

BEFORE THIS HIS MEN WENT ON HUNGER STRIKE TO EXPRESS THEIR LOYALTY.
THIS ACT OF DEFIANCE WAS BROUGHT TO A HALT BY NONE OTHER THAN SOSABOWSKI HIMSELF.

NEAR EDE, 14TH NOVEMBER

OPERATION PEGASUS

THE COAST IS CLEAR, COME. THEY'RE EXPECTING US...

WELCOME HERMAN. SEE ANYTHING SUSPICIOUS ON YOUR WAY OVER?

NO.

KNOCK KNOCK

COME IN...

THIS IS MAJOR DIGBY, THE MAN WHO MANAGED TO SMUGGLE 130 BRITISH OVER THE RHINE IN ONE GO.

AH, CODENAME OPERATION PEGASUS, I'VE HEARD ALL ABOUT IT.

DRINK?

AH, YES! SCHNAPPS!

NOT AT ALL, GOOD OLD DUTCH GIN, HOME BREWED!

AAH!! WONDERFUL STUFF!

COME, TELL US PLEASE.

NOW, SO AS YOU ALREADY KNOW, OUR GROUP WAS GETTING MORE AND MORE UNCOMFORTABLE, WITH THE LARGE NUMBER OF BRITISH TROOPS IN HIDING IN EDE...

43

ON FRIDAY 20TH OCTOBER WE RECEIVED WORD THAT BENNEKOM WAS TO BE EVACUATED. THE NEXT DAY THE ROADS WOULD BE FULL OF REFUGEES.

THIS WAS OUR CHANCE!

FIRST WE MOVED THE MEN IN TWOS AND THREES TO THE WOODS. THERE THEY GOT THEIR WEAPONS AND UNIFORMS BACK.

VERY IMPORTANT!

IF THEY WERE CAPTURED IN CIVILIAN CLOTHING THEY WOULD BE BRUTALLY SHOT AS SPIES.

WE DIVIDED THE WHOLE GROUP INTO SECTIONS AND PLATOONS. DIGBY HERE WAS IN CHARGE.

ALL WAS GOING WELL. THE LAST MILE WE HAD TO CROSS OPEN GROUND PRECISELY BETWEEN TWO ENEMY POSITIONS...

THE GERMANS MUST HAVE HEARD US. WE SOUNDED MORE LIKE A HERD OF BUFFALO THAN A DISCIPLINED ARMY CORPS.

HOWEVER THEY DID NOTHING.

WE REACHED THE RHINE BY MIDNIGHT AND GAVE THE AGREED SIGNAL.

AFTER TWENTY MINUTES THERE WAS STILL NO SIGN OF THE BOATS.

AN AMERICAN OFFICER SUDDENLY APPEARED AND EXPLAINED THAT THE BOATS WERE WAITING FOR US 400 YARDS TO THE WEST.

WE FOUND THE BOATS AND A BRITISH OFFICER WHO WAS IRRITATED THAT WE WERE SO LATE.

THE RHINE CROSSING WENT WITHOUT A HITCH.

AND NOW WE'RE BACK.

ANOTHER DRAM?

YES, PLEASE!

Thanks!

We received a lot of help while making this book. Financially and otherwise.
Therefore we would like to thank everyone involved. Our special thanks go out to: M. W. L. Vaessen Heijnen,
Wybo Boersma, Edo Veenstra, Jan Fokkema, Berry de Reus (Airborne Museum Oosterbeek),
Philip Reinders, Freddie Coenders.

With this book we have tried to describe part of the Battle of Arnhem. Due to limitations, we were forced to make choices summarising a sequence of events already described in more than a hundred published written books, into 44 illustrated pages.
This is not a scientific publication. Events are simplified, adapted and often depicted in a fictional manner.

Tine Bouwhuis and Hennie Vaessen

Bibliography:

George F. Cholewczynski
De Polen van Driel
1990 Uitgeverij Lunet

Kate A. ter Horst-Arriëns
Een schuilplaats in de pastorie
2009 Uitgeverij Kontrast

Joseph Levine
A Bridge too Far (film)
1977 MGM, 20th century Fox, UA

Karel Margry (editor)
Operation Market Garden, Then and Now
2002, Battle of Britain International Limited

Martin Middlebrook
Ooggetuigenverslagen van de Slag om Arnhem
1994 Tirion

Cornelius Ryan
A Bridge too Far
1974 Popular library edition

John Sliz
The wrong Side of the River
2010 Stormboatkings

Stanislaw Sosabowski
Ik vocht voor de vrijheid
1960 Sijthoff

F.J. Stevens
German Army Uniforms 1935-45
1978 Almark Publishing Co. Ltd.

Marek Swiecicki
Roode Duivels in Arnhem
1945 Elsevier

Visual material of numerous internet sites was used
as a reference.

Polish:

BOŹE DROGI	OH MY GOD
CHĘTNIE	WILLINGLY
CHOLERNE SZWABY	DAMN HUNS
DAWAJ	GIVE HERE
DO DIABŁA	HELL
DOBRA	GOOD
DOBRANOC	GOOD NIGHT
DZIĘKUJĘ	THANK YOU
GENERAŁOWIE	GENERALS
GENERAŁOWIE! Z CAŁYM SZACUNKIEM...	GENERALS, WITH ALL DUE RESPECT...
...NIE POŚWIĘCAJCIE NASZYCH ŻOŁNIERZY.	...DO NOT SACRIFICE OUR SOLDIERS.
JESTEŚMY POLACY	WE ARE POLISH
MATKO ŚWIĘTA	HOLY MOTHER
NIECH TO SZLAG	DAMN
POMOCY	HELP
POWODZENIA	GOOD LUCK
PROSZĘ	PLEASE
STAĆ	STOP
STÓJ	STOP
ŚWIĘTA MARYJO, MATKO BOŻA	HAIL MARY, FULL OF GRACE
ŚWINIE	THE SWINE
TAK	YES
TAK JEST	YES
TO TU	IT'S HERE
WARSZAWA	WARSAW
WITAMY	WELCOME
WOLNA POLSKA	FREE POLAND

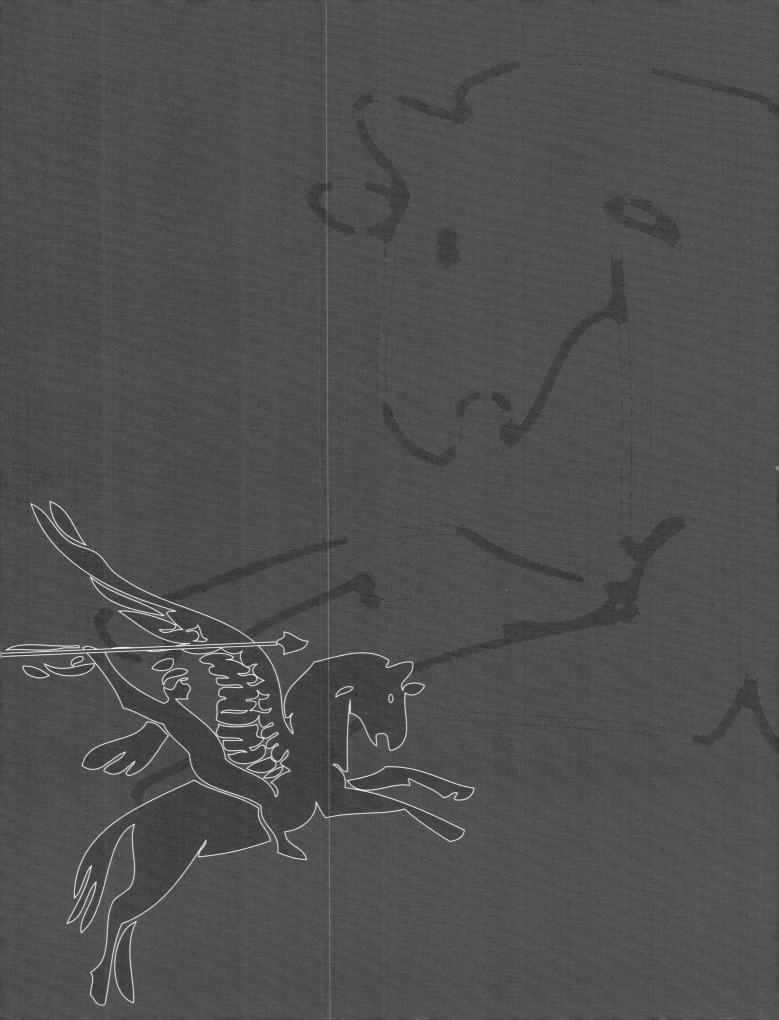